CHANGE *of*
HEART

Written by Josie Green

Illustrated by Marjorie Scott

CHANGE *of* HEART

Contents

Chapter 1
Bad News

Sam sat outside as the sun slowly started to go down. It was still warm and Sam felt good.

She had finished her homework and was now reading a book. She could hardly put it down. She was so lost in the story that she lost track of the time. It wasn't until Sam started to feel a little cold that she saw that it was getting dark.

"That's funny," she said to herself as she shivered a little.

"I wonder where Sharon is. She should be home by now. It's not like her to be late."

Sharon was Sam's stepmother. She got home soon after Sam got in from school. They talked and read. Then, around seven o'clock, Sharon would cook dinner. They always ate late because Sam's dad didn't get home from work till after eight.

As Sam turned around to check the time on the kitchen clock, her book fell to the floor.

"Oh no! That'll be a pain to pick up," Sam said out loud to no one at all. "I'll have to leave it for Sharon or Dad to grab when they get home."

Just then the doorbell rang. Sam pulled the lever on her chair and headed for the door to see who it was.

"I wonder who that is," she said. "Who could be visiting us at this time of day?"

She was able to move really fast in her new chair. She was so pleased when her dad had bought it for her. The old one had been so slow.

Sam quickly got to the door and opened it.

"Hello, Mary," she said, when she saw who it was at the door. "Come on in. Sharon's not home yet. Is there something I can do for you?"

As Sam looked up at Mary's face she could see that something was very wrong.

"It's your father, Sam," Mary said. "He's in the hospital. Sharon wants me to take you over there right away."

"What is it?" asked Sam.

She felt sick inside. She had spent a lot of time in hospitals herself, so she knew all about them. But she still hated them.

Sharon was waiting for them at the hospital. Her eyes were filled with tears. Sam felt a feeling of panic swamping her.

"Sam, your father's had a heart attack," Sharon said.

Chapter 2
At the Hospital

"No, no, no!" Sam cried, over and over again.

"It's all right, Sam," Sharon said, being brave. "The doctor said he's going to be OK."

"Can I see him?" Sam sobbed. "I want to see him."

"Of course you can," Sharon replied, giving Sam a hug. "But he's sleeping and we can't wake him."

"But we can go and see him, can't we?" asked Sam.

"The doctor says that we can go and sit by his bed," said Sharon. "But we have to be very quiet."

As they made their way to the room where Sam's dad was, Sam asked Sharon what had happened.

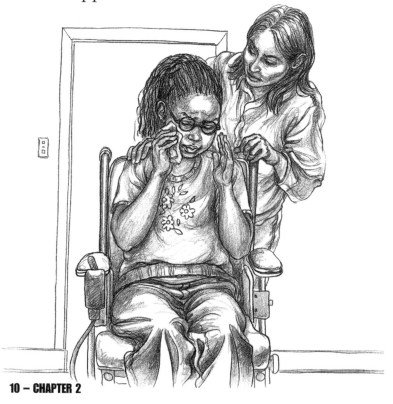

"I'm not really sure," Sharon replied. "Jack's boss called me just after lunch. He said your dad had had a heart attack at work."

"Did he fall over and hurt himself?" asked Sam.

"I don't know," replied Sharon. "By the time I got to your dad's work, he was on the way to the hospital. I didn't wait around to ask what had happened. I came over here right away."

"What time did this happen?" asked Sam.

"About two hours ago," replied Sharon. "I couldn't call you before because I had to fill out all sorts of forms and answer questions."

"That's OK," replied Sam. "I know all about filling out forms."

"They ran a lot of tests on your dad," said Sharon. "He's resting now. But you need to prepare yourself, Sam. He doesn't look too good."

Regardless of the warning Sharon had given her, Sam sucked in her breath as she entered her dad's room. She was shocked by what she saw.

Chapter 3

Tubes and Wires

Sam was shocked at how old her father looked. Her dad seemed to have aged ten years since she had seen him that morning.

"Is he going to die?" she asked through her tears. Sharon put her arm around Sam's shoulders.

"No, Sam," she said. "The attack wasn't as bad as they first thought it was. We were very lucky that your dad's boss was still at work. If he had gone home there would have been no one there to help your dad."

Sam wheeled her chair to the side of her dad's bed and held his hand. He looked dreadful. Sam felt as though someone had kicked her in the stomach. This was her dad. He could not die! Her whole body started to shake. She began to sob loudly.

She could feel Sharon holding her, but it was little comfort. All she could do was cry.

"Come on, Sam," Sharon said gently through her own tears. "He'll bounce back. In no time at all he'll be back to his old self again. Just you wait and see."

"Are you sure?" Sam asked.

It was hard to tell how long they sat there in silence. Soon, both Sam and Sharon ran out of tears. There were none left to shed. They just sat there and looked as Jack breathed in and out into his oxygen mask.

"It would be better if you both went home," a nurse said as she checked the machines in the room. "Jack won't wake up until tomorrow. Go and get some sleep. He'll need your strength in the morning."

"I want to stay here," said Sam. "I don't want to go home. I want to stay here with Dad."

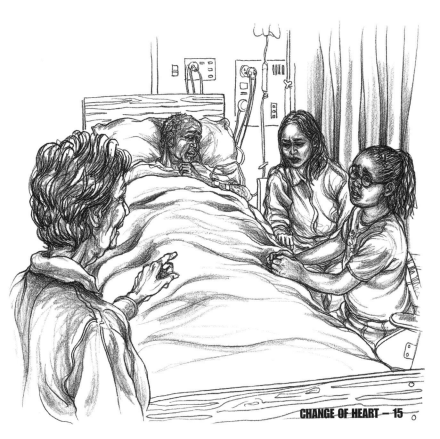

"The nurse is right, Sam," Sharon said. "Come on. We'll come back first thing in the morning."

That night, Sam couldn't sleep. She could still see her father with all those tubes coming out of his body. He had always joked that he was as strong as an ox. He wasn't very strong now.

Chapter 4

Things to Think About

Doctor Chang had been Sam's family doctor for years. He was a kind gentle man. But this morning he was like he had never been before. He was really stern. His face was dark as storm clouds. He started with Sam's dad.

"You need to make some big changes to you lifestyle," he said bluntly. "I've told you this before, but you didn't listen. Now your body's telling you. If you don't change your lifestyle, you won't be around for Sam's 12th birthday next year!"

"What do you mean?" Jack asked. "Of course I'll be around for Sam's birthday."

"You won't if you don't change your lifestyle," Doctor Chang said again. "You eat the wrong food at the wrong times. You're overweight and you don't exercise. You work too much and you're stressed. You should think about getting fit. Then you should get back into basketball. You're a good player, you know."

Jack was stunned. At first he could say nothing. It was taking quite a while for all this information to sink in. Then he said, "I don't have time for that anymore. I need to work long hours just to make ends meet."

"Make time," Doctor Chang said.

Then it was Sharon's turn. Doctor Chang was still looking very stern as he spoke.

"What Jack needs is plenty of support from you," Doctor Chang said. "You will have to help him change his diet. He needs to eat three healthy meals a day. He can't go on missing breakfast and lunch. He also needs to get some exercise."

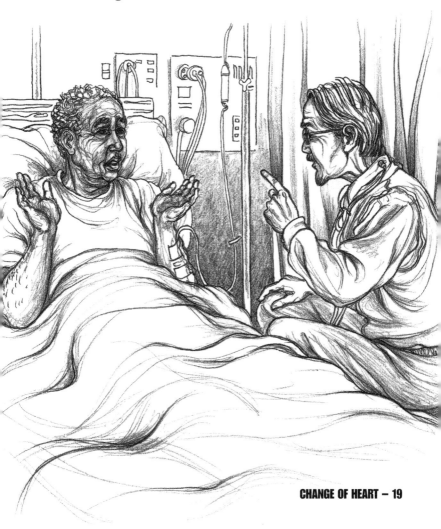

Then Doctor Chang turned to Sam.

"Now, Sam," he said. "You can help your dad, too."

Sam was shocked by what Doctor Chang was saying. The doctor knew she was in a wheelchair. How would she possibly be able to help her father?

"What do you mean?" she asked.

"Think about it," Doctor Chang replied. "There are many things that I know you leave other people to do. There's a lot more that you could do for yourself."

"But…" Sam started to say.

"No buts," replied the doctor. "Your dad is coming home tomorrow. You all need to do a lot of thinking tonight."

Chapter 5
Bad Habits

Sam and Sharon fussed over Jack during his first week at home. Sam tried really hard not to ask him to do anything for her. Her dad seemed to love every minute of it, but then he said he was going back to work.

"You can't go back to work yet," Sharon said. "You have to take it easy for a little while."

"I won't work long hours," replied Jack. "I'll be home early."

Sam knew her dad was going to find it hard to change his lifestyle. She was right.

After a month she could already see that he was slipping back into his old habits. By the sixth week he was starting to work late again. He was also skipping breakfast and lunch and Sam knew that he wasn't doing any exercise.

"Why is he doing this?" Sam asked herself.

And then one night she heard Sharon and her dad talking and she knew why.

It was after Sam had gone to bed. Jack and Sharon were in the kitchen. Sam was thirsty so she got out of bed to get a drink. She froze as she heard what they said.

"Jack, don't work any more overtime," Sharon said.

"You know I have to," Sam's dad replied. "It's the only way I can cover the cost of the things that Sam needs. Now it's the repayments on Sam's new wheelchair."

Sam felt sick. She had never even stopped to think her father worked the long hours to pay for things for her. She knew that the new high-tech wheelchair was expensive. She had never thought that her father couldn't afford it.

"Why did he buy me the wheelchair? " said Sam to herself. "Why didn't he just say we couldn't afford it?"

But then she remembered that she had gone on and on about her old wheelchair. She had moaned that it was too heavy. She had moaned that it was too slow. She had moaned and moaned and moaned. Her dad had never said a word. And then one day he had come home from work with a new high-tech chair.

Sam went to her room and started to cry. She felt so useless. There must be some way she could help.

Then she remembered what Doctor Chang had said. Her dad wouldn't live to see her 12th birthday if he didn't change his lifestyle. And the only way for him to change his lifestyle was for Sam to do more things for herself.

She stopped crying.

"I've got to stop thinking of myself as disabled," she said aloud. "I need to get fit. Then I'll have more energy to do things for myself. That will take the stress off Dad and Sharon."

So Sam thought up a plan.

Chapter 6

Step One

Sam rang Doctor Chang on Saturday and told him her plan.

"I need to get fit just as much as Dad does," Sam said. "I know he'll do anything for me. So if I ask him to help me get fit, I know he will. That way he'll get fit, too."

"Start slowly," Doctor Chang told Sam. "In fact, start very slowly. Get your dad to walk first. And make sure he walks slowly. And make it fun for both of you, otherwise you won't keep it up."

So Sam put step one of her plan into action.

After lunch she wheeled herself down to her dad's work. He looked surprised to see her. He was even more surprised to see that she was in her old wheelchair. But he didn't say anything.

"I'm going down to watch the Kings play. Do you want to come along?" Sam asked her dad.

She knew her dad would say yes because he loved basketball, and he loved watching the Kings play.

"Sure," Jack said. Then he packed up his work and headed for the van.

"Hey, Dad, it's a nice day," Sam said. "Why don't we walk down to the game instead of driving?"

Jack looked surprised but said nothing. He just nodded in agreement. So they left the van behind and went on down the hill.

Sam and her dad had a great time at the game. Jack really got into it. Sam had never seen her dad at a basketball game before. She was surprised at how happy he was.

He shouted in protest whenever he thought the referee had made an unfair call.

"No, Ref! No!" he shouted when the ref blew his whistle. "That wasn't a foul."

And he yelled out in praise when one of the players shot a basket.

"Great basket!" he shouted. "Did you see that, Sam?"

On the way back to the van Sam asked her dad about when he played basketball.

"Tell me about the time that you used to play basketball, Dad," said Sam. "I was too little to remember. Did I come and watch you play?"

Jack chatted all the way back to the van. "It was a good time in my life, Sam," he said. "It was a time that I really loved."

Sam couldn't remember when he had talked this much. The only time he stopped talking was when he needed to have a rest to get his breath.

Sam was glad that her dad needed to stop now and again because she was also quite tired. Her arms were aching with the strain of wheeling her chair up the hills. She had forgotten just how hard it was using the old chair.

Her father had offered to push her but she turned him down. She had to do this for herself as well as for him. As her dad lifted her into the van Sam noticed the sweat running down his face. They were both in bad shape.

As they were driving home Sam asked her dad why he had stopped playing basketball. There was a long moment of silence. Sam looked at her dad. She could see his eyes misting over.

"I left the team right after the accident," he said softly. "I didn't feel like playing anymore."

"Oh," Sam replied, feeling as sad as her dad looked.

"If the truck driver had stayed awake he wouldn't have collided with our car," Sam's dad said. "Then your mother would still be alive. And you wouldn't be in a wheelchair."

"And more than likely you wouldn't have just had a heart attack," Sam thought. But she said nothing. They drove home in silence.

"Well, something good is going to come of this," Sam thought as her dad helped her out of the van. "I'm going to be independent so Dad doesn't have to work so hard. Maybe I can even get him to take up basketball again."

Chapter 7
Step Two

On Sunday morning, Sam started on the next part of her plan. She found her dad reading the paper.

"What are your plans for after school on Tuesday?" she asked. "If you're free I need your help."

Jack dropped his paper. "What do you need me to do, Sam?" he asked.

"I need to get into better shape," Sam replied. "I've been really short of breath."

"So how can I help you?" her dad asked, as Sam knew he would.

"There's a walking track around the park," said Sam. "But there's one hill I can't seem to get up. Do you think you could come with me and help me up the hill?"

"Sure," he agreed, as Sam knew he would. "I'll just take a late lunch hour. We can do it then."

"Thanks, Dad," said Sam, hugging him. "You're special."

The walk in the park went really well. Sam had a great time.

"Dad, can we do this again, please?" Sam asked.

"I could take another late lunch on Thursday," Jack replied.

On the way home Sam said, "I'm using the old wheelchair so that I can get more exercise."

"I thought so," Jack replied.

"I don't get to use my arms much in the new chair," Sam said.

She hoped her dad didn't feel too bad about the fact that she wasn't using her new chair. But then he didn't know that she had overheard him talking to Sharon.

"That's fine," Jack said.

"You could sell the new wheelchair if you like," Sam said.

"I don't think so, Sam," her dad replied. "The old one is pretty hard work. Let's see how fit you get first. Then we'll talk about what to do with the new wheelchair."

On Friday morning, Sam got dressed by herself. It was a struggle, but she did it. Then she got herself into her wheelchair and went to the kitchen.

"I was just coming to help you," her dad said, doing a double take.

Sam just smiled.

"Fruit and cereal for both of you," Sharon said. "You'll have time for breakfast, Jack, now that you don't have to help Sam."

'That sounds just fine," replied Jack. "I guess Sam and I could start with orange juice, too. What do you say, Sam? Do you want some orange juice?"

"Yes, please," Sam said. She was already feeling better because her dad had time for breakfast.

"Looks like my plan is working," she thought.

"Dad," said Sam. "It's a great day out there. What if you walk to work and I come with you? Then tonight I'll meet you and we can come home together?"

"That's a good idea," said Sharon, smiling at them.

Jack looked at Sharon and smiled as well. Then he turned back to Sam and said, "You're on. But I have to be at work by eight o'clock, so eat up."

"And tomorrow there's another home basketball game," Sam said. "Can we go to it?"

"Are you saying that I've got to walk all the way up and down that hill again," Jack asked with a smile.

"Please, Dad," Sam said. "I really enjoyed the Kings game the other day. I'd like to go again."

"Oh, all right, then," Jack replied. "I suppose that next you'll want me to play basketball again."

"Now that really would be something," Sam replied.

And so it became a routine. Sam went to and from work with her father on all the days that the weather was good. They walked in the park after school two days a week. And on Saturday they found a basketball game to go to.

Chapter 8
The Good Life

Seven months later, Sam and Sharon sat at the sideline watching Jack play basketball. He was so fast up and down the court, shooting baskets, and making great saves. Sam couldn't believe it was the same man who had had a heart attack nearly a year ago.

Who would have thought this was the same person that lay in a hospital bed? Who would believe that he might not be around now if he had carried on the way he was going?

It turned out that Sam's plan had worked better than she could have ever imagined. Both she and her dad were now in great shape.

Sharon had joined in after the first month. Soon Jack and Sharon had stepped up the pace so that they were walking and jogging. In no time at all they were jogging all the time.

Again, Sam asked her dad to sell the new wheelchair.

"This one is helping my fitness," she said. "My arms are really strong now. They're so strong that I can keep up with you and Sharon when you jog."

"OK, Sam," he said. "We'll sell the new wheelchair."

Sam smiled. Her plan was working.

Sam's dad was so excited about their exercise routine that he put a training schedule on the fridge. He even bought a pulse monitor so that he could chart everyone's progress.

As Sam and her dad became fitter, other parts of their lives changed, too. Sam was able to do more and more for herself. By now, Sam could get herself showered and dressed in the mornings. She had also learned to make her own bed.

She never ever asked anyone to do anything for her these days. Unless she really couldn't do something of course. And she never ever asked someone to pick up something she had dropped.

"How could I ever have done that?" Sam wondered.

This all meant that her dad had more free time. He used that time to eat properly, exercise, and relax.

"I can't remember ever having time for breakfast before," he said one day as he sat down to eat with Sharon and Sam. "And you know what else? Since I've been fitter I can get more done at work so I can take time for lunch."

"And now that you've sold the wheelchair you don't have to work overtime," Sam said.

As Sam and Sharon sat watching Jack on the basketball court, Sam realized how good she felt. At first she hadn't really noticed it. It wasn't until she looked back at what she used to be like that she knew just how far she'd come. She now had more energy, tried new things, and took on new challenges.

"Dad," Sam said as he came off the court at the end of the game. "Do you know what I really want to do for my birthday?"

"No," replied her dad. "But tell me and I'll see what I can do to make it happen."

"I want to play basketball," Sam said. "There's a wheelchair-basketball team that meets here on Tuesday evenings. The problem is, the coach has just left. If the team doesn't find a new coach and some more players, it might fold."

"No problem, Sam," Jack said and smiled a big smile at his daughter. He knew exactly what she meant.